O N E

I saw someone at the bookstore buying *One-Punch Man*. I couldn't help but stare. I'm not some kind of weirdo.

—ONE

Manga creator ONE began *One-Punch Man* as a webcomic, which quickly went viral, garnering over 10 million hits. In addition to *One-Punch Man*, ONE writes and draws the series *Mob Psycho 100* and *Makai no Ossan*.

YUSUKE MURATA
(AND THE CURRENT MEMBERS OF VILLAGE STUDIO)

The elite members of the studio continue to aim for new heights and polish their skills every day. If one looks like he's asleep, that's just your imagination.

—Yusuke Murata

A highly decorated and skilled artist best known for his work on *Eyeshield 21*, Yusuke Murata won the 122nd Hop Step Award (1995) for *Partner* and placed second in the 51st Akatsuka Award (1998) for *Samui Hanashi*.

ONE-PUNCH MAN

04

STORY BY
ONE

ART BY
YUSUKE
MURATA

▶TANK-TOP
TIGER

▶BANG

▶S·A·I·T·A·M·A

CHARACTERS

▶ GENOS

▶ SONIC

A single man arose to face the evil threatening humankind!
His name was Saitama. He became a hero for fun.

Saitama went with Genos to take the professional hero exam and passed with
flying colors on his first try! Now he begins his service as a new Class-C hero.

But he wasn't aware of his quota of one heroic deed per week, so he is
suddenly faced with the crisis of losing his registration! As he races around
town looking for trouble, he runs into Speed-o'-Sound Sonic. Sonic wreaks
havoc on the city, and Saitama defeats him, but...

STORY

STRAW-
BERRY
SYRUP

CONTENTS

ONE-PUNCH MAN VOLUME FOUR

ONE-PUNCH MAN

ONE + YUSUKE MURATA

My name is Saitama. I am a hero. My hobby is heroic exploits. I got too strong. And that makes me sad. I can defeat any enemy with one blow. I lost my hair. And I lost all feeling. I want to feel the rush of battle. I would like to meet an incredibly strong enemy. And I would like to defeat it with one blow. That's because I am One-Punch Man.

04

GIANT METEOR

HMM...

GENOS HAS A SUBSCRIPTION.
↓

SO IT WENT UP AFTER THAT FIGHT THE OTHER DAY?

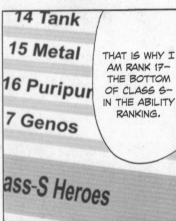

14 Tank

15 Metal

16 Puripur

7 Genos

ass-S Heroes

THAT IS WHY I AM RANK 17— THE BOTTOM OF CLASS S— IN THE ABILITY RANKING.

NO, NOT YET.

GULP

IT'S BEEN A WEEK. HAVE YOU DONE ANY HEROIC DEEDS?

SPURT

WHY?!

BUT IN THE WEEKLY POPULARITY RANKING VOTED ON BY CITIZENS, I AM NUMBER SIX.

"A SENSE OF FRAGILITY UNDER THE STEELY EXPRESSION."

"EXPECT MUCH FROM THIS GENIUS WHO DEBUTED IN CLASS S AT THE YOUNG AGE OF 19."

"HIS FACE IS GORGEOUS..."

"AMONG THE TOP FIVE BEST-LOOKING HEROES."

"HE'S THE CYBORG PRINCE."

"I LOVE THE COOL WAY HE REFUSES ALL MEDIA CONTACT."

RIGHT... OF COURSE...

THOSE COMMENTS WERE BASED MERELY ON MY PHOTO. THEY DO NOT REALLY KNOW ME, SO I DO NOT MIND.

AND SO ON.

DOESN'T IT EMBARRASS YOU TO READ ALL THAT?

9

CUT THE FLATTERY. IT'S DISGUSTING.

I HAVE NEVER SEEN ANYONE AS INCREDIBLE AS YOU, MASTER, EVEN IF THE WORLD DOES NOT KNOW IT.

FOR SOME REASON, THE HERO ASSOCIATION IS SUMMONING ME.

I MUST GO.

OH!

MAYBE YOU'RE FIRED! HA HA!

...IS A CLASS-S, RANK-3 HERO.

...

BANG...

HE POSSESSES TRUE SKILL.

I CAME BECAUSE THE ASSOCIATION CALLED ME.

TMP

THIS BRANCH OFFICE IS EMPTY.

EVERYONE IN THE ASSOCIATION HAS EVACUATED.

HW_o o o o o o o

WE ARE THE ONLY TWO CLASS-S HEROES TO COME.

I SUPPOSE THE OTHERS WERE TOO FAR AWAY OR BUSY.

SOME PROBABLY JUST COULDN'T BE BOTHERED.

WHY DID THE OTHERS NOT COME?

THEY EVACUATED? WHY?

WHY DID THEY SUMMON ME?

THIS IS SURE TO BE MORE THAN WE CAN HANDLE.

SUMMONS ONLY GO OUT FOR THE BIGGEST, MOST IMPOSSIBLE TASKS.

A METEOR ?!

THIS TIME, THE PROBLEM'S TOO BIG.

DOES THE POPULACE KNOW?

YOU SHOULD FLEE WITH THOSE YOU CARE ABOUT.

...SO THE FIRST REPORTS MUST BE GOING OUT ABOUT NOW.

THEIR PLAN WAS TO ISSUE AN EVACUATION WARNING TO THE IMPACT AREA THIRTY MINUTES BEFOREHAND...

HA HA! IT'LL BE MASS PANIC!

GRIN

...WARNING...

...A WARNING!

...HAS ISSUED...

THE HERO ASSOCIATION HAS ISSUED...

WHAT WILL YOU DO, OLD FELLOW?

ADDRESS ME AS MR. BANG.

Z CITY BRANCH....

HERO A

AH...

There it is...

20

...

RUN AS QUICKLY AND AS FAR AS YOU CAN!

I WANTED A GIRLFRIEND BEFORE I DIED...

WOOOOOOO O

WE'RE DOOMED ...

IT'S HUGE ...

MANY ARE GIVING UP ON SURVIVAL.

THE SUR-ROUNDING TOWNS WILL ALSO BE DESTROYED!

THIS IS ABOUT MORE THAN CITY Z...

CLIK

TCH!

AND IT IS TOO LATE TO EVACUATE!

BEEP

ARMS MODE

IT IS TIME TO TEST THIS PROTOTYPE...

DOES HE LIVE IN CITY Z TOO? OR HAS HE RISKED HIS LIFE TO COME HERE?

THIS CLASS-S, RANK-7 HERO USES MASSIVE FIREPOWER TO DEMOLISH HIS ENEMIES— ALONG WITH ANY BUILDINGS IN THE VICINITY!

Y-YOU...

YES.

BOFOI. WORK TOGETHER WITH ME.

ARE YOU THE NEW HERO GENOS?

HAVE YOU COME TO STOP THE METEOR?

NO.

TEST? THIS IS NOT THE TIME.

WHY NOT?

IF THE METEOR STRIKES, YOU WILL DIE.

NO, I WILL NOT.

I MERELY CAME TO TEST A NEW WEAPON.

WHAT?

THE METEOR IS A CONVENIENT TARGET.

...TO A REMOTE-CONTROLLED ROBOT.

RIGHT NOW, YOU ARE TALKING...

NO METEOR'S KILLING *ME*.

SORRY, BUT I'M NOT RISKING MY LIFE.

CALL ME *THE METAL KNIGHT*.

AND DO NOT CALL ME BOFOI.

HEROES ADDRESS EACH OTHER BY THEIR HERO NAMES. THAT IS COMMON SENSE.

TCH!

!

RRMM

BUT...

...THERE IS NO MORE TIME FOR TALK.

WHSH

44

YOU ARE TOO YOUNG TO WORRY ABOUT FAILURE.

I CAN SEE YOU ARE UNSETTLED.

THE OUTCOME WON'T CHANGE, SO THAT'S BEST.

IN A PINCH, JUST MUDDLE THROUGH.

...IS BEST?

MUDDLING THROUGH...

RRII

HMM...

GRB

IPP

THIS IS *MY* TOWN ...

THREE DAYS LATER

CITY Z ESCAPED TOTAL ANNIHILATION BY THE IMPACT OF A GIANT METEOR...

...BUT SUFFERED WIDESPREAD DAMAGE DUE TO A SHOWER OF DEBRIS WHEN THE METEOR WAS DESTROYED.

...YOU AND THE METAL KNIGHT COULD HAVE COOPERATED TO KEEP THE DAMAGE TO A MINIMUM.

IF THE HERO ASSOCIATION HAD ASKED YOU INSTEAD OF ME FOR HELP...

DON'T FRET OVER IT.

HE COULDN'T HAVE TEAMED UP WITH ANYBODY.

BUT THAT GUY WAS ONLY LOOKING OUT FOR HIMSELF.

NO ONE DIED, DID THEY?

I *DID* KEEP THE DAMAGE DOWN.

HE IS RIGHT.

ONE PUNCH FROM MASTER DECREASED THE METEOR'S FORCE AND LESSENED THE SHOCK WAVE.

OTHERWISE, EVEN IF PEOPLE HAD HIDDEN IN EVACUATION SHELTERS OR FLED TO THE SUBURBS, THE METEOR'S SHOCK WAVE WOULD HAVE BLOWN EVERYTHING AWAY.

...WHILE YOU ARE UNAWARE OF IT, MASTER...

BUT...

THE PEOPLE SHOULD EXTOL HIM AS A HERO FOR AGES TO COME.

WHAT HE DID WAS A MIRACLE.

...CONSIDERS YOU TO BE A VILLAIN RESPONSIBLE FOR THE PARTIAL DESTRUCTION OF CITY Z.

...MUCH OF THE WORLD...

BLUH

IN TIME, CITY Z WILL RECOVER AND THE COMPLAINTS WILL CEASE.

I MUST NOT TELL HIM.

OUR RANKINGS WENT UP, RIGHT?

I ALMOST FORGOT.

FAMP

YOU MOVED FROM CLASS C, RANK 342 TO RANK 5.

I MOVED FROM CLASS S, RANK 17 TO RANK 16.

HUH? OH... YES.

THE METAL KNIGHT WENT FROM CLASS S, RANK 7 TO RANK 6.

SORCH SORCH

FROM 342 TO 5?! WHAT THE-?! ISN'T THAT WEIRD?!

...BECAUSE THE THREAT LEVEL WAS *DRAGON*.

NO. EVEN MOVING FROM CLASS A TO CLASS S WOULD HAVE BEEN UNDERSTANDABLE...

SIMPLY DESTROYING THE METEOR SHOULD HAVE LANDED YOU IN CLASS A, BUT THE HERO ASSOCIATION HAS ASSUMED THAT THE METAL KNIGHT AND I PLAYED AN IMPORTANT ROLE.

...N...N...

HUH...N...

HAD YOU ALSO PREVENTED DAMAGE FROM THE DEBRIS, YOU WOULD HAVE JUMPED TO ABOUT CLASS S, RANK 5.

DOES THAT MEAN SOMETHING?

THE MEDIA ALWAYS TALKS ABOUT THREAT LEVELS LIKE DEMON AND TIGER.

...

Threat Level

God: A crisis threatening the extinction of humankind.

Dragon: A crisis threatening destruction of multiple towns.

Demon: A crisis threatening to interrupt a town's functioning or destroy it altogether.

Tiger: A crisis threatening massive loss of life.

Wolf: Appearance of a life-form or group posing a risk.

A HERO WOULD USUALLY TAKE THAT INTO CONSIDERATION WHEN DECIDING WHETHER TO GO INTO ACTION...

...BUT I GUESS YOU DO NOT CARE.

YES.

WHO'S GONNA FIGHT IF ALL THE HEROES RUN AWAY?

NO, I CARE!

I MUST WRITE THAT DOWN!

SKRK SKRK SKRK SKRK SKRK SRRK

WHOA, WHAT'RE YOU DOING?

KA

KLIK

...I THINK I'LL TAKE A LITTLE WALK.

ALL RIGHT...

IF THAT'S WHAT IT TAKES TO RAISE MY RANK...

SKRK SKRK SKRK

HMM...

SWIP

BUT MY OLD LAND-LORD'S BUILDING IS FINE? TCH!

AGH! THE SUPER-MARKET IS IN RUINS!

I'VE SEEN SOME DESTROYED TOWNS IN MY DAY...

THIS PLACE IS A WRECK...

...BUT IT SUCKS WHEN IT HAPPENS TO MY TOWN.

HUH?

HEY!

TUMP

WHAT'RE YOU DOIN' HERE...

...YOU *FRAUD.*

DON'T FORGET ME, YOU NEWB!

TANK-TOP TIGER!

UH... WHO ARE YOU?

I WON'T STAND FOR *LIES.*

BUT YOU SAY YOU PLAYED A BIG ROLE?

YOU'RE THE CLASS-C NOBODY WHO WORKED WITH CLASS-S HEROES TO DESTROY THE METEOR.

YO, BIG BROOOOOOO!!!

THIS TIME WAS NOTHING.

IT'S NOT A LIE.

I DON'T CARE ABOUT THREAT LEVEL DEMON OR DRAGON OR WHATNOT. I DO THAT STUFF ALL THE TIME.

THAT'S TOTAL BALONEY!

AND YOU'RE GONNA REGRET IT.

YOU AIN'T ON OUR LEVEL, MAN! SO WATCH YOUR MOUTH!

MY BIG BRO'S A CLASS-B HIGH-RANKER AND A FIRST-RATE TANK-TOPPER!

WHAT'S A TANK-TOPPER?

...WHO IS THIS GUY?

SERI-OUSLY...

I FOUND YOU-KNOW-WHO!

ARE YOU THE FRAUD WHO CLINGS TO CLASS-S HEROES AND STEALS THE CREDIT TO IMPROVE YOUR RANK?!

AREN'T YOU *ASHAMED*?! HUH?!

ONLY A *FAKE* COULD CLIMB THE RANKS SO FAST.

EVERY-ONE IN CLASS C HATES YOU!

HUH? GIMME A BREAK.

...WHAT DO YOU WANT?

SO, UH...

HMM... I SEE...

SOME GUYS ARE LIKE THIS.

IT'S *TIGER*! GRAH!

TANK-TOP CIDER JUST MADE THAT UP.

ZING ZANG

WHY'S HE YELLING?

OH, I GET IT! SOME TOWNS-PEOPLE WOULD GET ANGRY AT THIS GUY.

?!

WHAT A HORRIBLE GUY YOU ARE!!

...WOULD BE DEVASTATING !!!

USING THAT AGAINST HIM...

I CAN'T BELIEVE A HERO WOULD DO SUCH A THING!

HE'S RIGHT...

...

LOOK AROUND! *YOU* DID THIS!

THEY TOOK THE BAIT!!!

THIS IS YOUR FAULT!

TH...

THOSE ARE THE *PAINED CRIES* OF THE *DISPLACED*!!

CAN YOU HEAR THAT?!

YOU BEAST!

YEAH!

DON'T YOU EVEN *WANT* TO ACCEPT RESPONSIBILITY?!

YEAH ...

YEAH! YEAH!

YOUR *RASH BEHAVIOR* RESULTED IN ALL THIS *SUFFERING!*

YOU SHOULD GIVE UP...

...BEING A HERO!

GIVE IT UP!

GIVE IT UP!

GIVE IT UP!

GIVE IT UP!

GIVE IT UP!

GIVE IT UP!

110

GWO O O

GET LOST!

GET LOST!

SAITAMA...

...BUT THIS IS HOW THEY REACT.

...YOU SAVED THIS TOWN...

GET LOST!

GET LOST!

GET LOST!

THIS IS *REALITY.*

GET LOST!

GET LOST!

QUITTING IS ONE POSSIBLE PATH.

SO I WON'T SAY ANYTHING HERE.

I DON'T WANT TO SEE YOU WASTE AWAY IN THIS PROFESSION!

YOU ARE PERHAPS THE STRONGEST I HAVE EVER ENCOUNTERED.

THEY PLAN TO CRUSH THE NEW GUY...

...AS A PUBLICITY STUNT FOR THEMSELVES.

THOSE YOUNG ONES IN THE TANK TOPS ARE TOO GREEDY.

...AND NEVER MAKE IT PAST CLASS B.

I SHOULD GO.

THEY'LL FLAME OUT IN THE FINAL STRETCH...

YOU'RE A STAIN ON HEROES! SO WE'RE GONNA WIPE YOU AWAY!!!

TANK-TOP TIGER FIGHTS LIKE A TIGER...

...AND TANK-TOP BLACK HOLE HAS A CRUSHING, 200-KILO-GRAM GRIP!

GRAAAH!

119

IF YOU WANNA HATE ME, THEN HATE ME!! YOU BALDIES!!

WHAT DO I CARE ABOUT THE DAMAGE?!

YOU'RE THE BALDY.

...

ANY MORE COMPLAINTS? I'LL TALK BACK, THOUGH!!

BUT I DID THE RIGHT THING.

SHUT U-U-U-U-U-U-U-P!

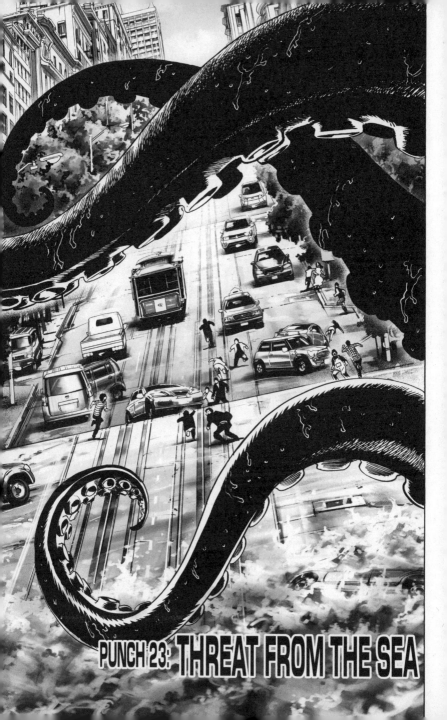

PUNCH 23: THREAT FROM THE SEA

RUMB...

MASTER, YOUR RANK HAS RISEN TO CLASS C, RANK 2.

THEN I WON'T HAVE TO DO ONE HEROIC DEED PER WEEK ANYMORE.

SPSHS

CLASS B?

SOON YOU CAN ADVANCE TO CLASS B.

SPSHS

IF YOU REACH CLASS C, RANK 1, YOU CAN BECOME A B-RANKER ...

... BUT YOU COULD ALSO REMAIN AT CLASS C, RANK 1.

CLINK

VWOO

COR-RECT.

THE CURRENT CLASS-C, RANK-1 HERO HAS NOT RISEN INTO CLASS B IN OVER HALF A YEAR.

CLINK

RRING

THAT HERO...

EVEN WORSE IS THE CURRENT CLASS-B, RANK-1 HERO.

I SEE. UNDERSTOOD.

ARE NO CAPABLE HEROES NEARBY?

I MAY NOT ARRIVE IN TIME, BUT I WILL LEAVE NOW.

CITY J? THAT IS A LITTLE FAR...

HE'S SO BUSY.

PARDON ME.

HELLO?

SOME MONSTERS CLAIMING TO BE HIS CLAN MEMBERS ARE RAMPAGING IN CITY J.

A CLASS-A HERO IS HAVING TROUBLE FIGHTING THEM ALONE.

DID THAT MONSTER YOU DEFEATED LAST WEEK SAY HE WAS FROM THE CLAN OF THE SEAFOLK?

I DON'T REMEMBER.

GENOS

ARE THEY STRONG?

BIP

TROUBLE?

MONSTERS APPEAR AT CITY J SEASIDE!

THE CREATURES APPEARING IN CITY J CLAIM TO BE FROM THE CLAN OF THE SEAFOLK.

THEY ATTACK ANYONE THEY SEE. A HERO IS ATTEMPTING TO PREVENT THEIR ADVANCE...

THREAT LEVEL TIGER!!! CITIZENS, STAY AWAY!

...BUT HE MAY BE AT HIS LIMIT. HE LOOKS EXHAUSTED.

WE'LL HAVE TO HURRY.

SHALL WE GO?

QUA-
DRUPLE
THRUST
!!

DID I JUST SINGLE-HANDEDLY BEAT A GOD-LEVEL INVASION?! I'M SO AW-W-W-WE-SOME!!

I DID IT... I DID IT!

...

PUNCH 24: **DEEP SEA KING**

EMERGENCY EVACUATION ALERT!

THE ATTACK BY THE CLAN OF THE SEAFOLK HAS RAISED THE THREAT LEVEL FROM TIGER TO DEMON!

WAAH

KYAH

RESIDENTS OF CITY J! EVACUATE AS FAR AS YOU CAN!

ENCOUNTERING A SEAPERSON IS MORE LIKELY ALONG THE COAST, SO...

I'LL RETURN THE KILLING OF MY SOLDIERS 100 MILLION TIMES OVER!

FWAP

FWAP

I WON'T LET *ANY* OF YOU ESCAPE.

TCH!

...

IT LOOKS LIKE STINGER HAS PASSED OUT.

AM I TOO LATE?

THAT HURT.

W...

WHAT THE HECK?!

WHAT'S THE BIG IDEA?

AND MY KICK PACKED WITH EXPLOSIVES DIDN'T WORK?

I WAS SO STARTLED I MADE A *WEIRD* SOUND!

HOW'D HE GET BEHIND ME?

UGH...

I CAN'T FEEL ANYTHING... I CAN'T MOVE... AM I SAFE NOW?

I CAN'T BREATHE... AM I IN THE BUILDING ACROSS THE STREET?

NO, THAT'S... AN EARTHQUAKE?

UH-OH...

HE'S BREAKING THE BUILDING?!

I' GOTTA GET OUT OF HERE...

ARGH...

KWAM

THANKS.

?!

YOU'RE PRISONER 4188.

I WAS DOING 10,000 YEARS FOR GETTING GRABBY WITH MEN!

SUR-PRISED? I KEEP TABS ON GUYS WHO STRIKE MY FANCY.

YOU NEED TO BE LOCKED UP...

I'M SURPRISED A BRAND-NEW CLASS-C HERO...

...COULD BRING DOWN SUCH A NASTY ASSASSIN.

THE HOLDING CENTER HAD A HARD TIME.

HE ALWAYS SLIPPED OFF HIS CUFFS...

...AND ATTACKED HIS CELLMATES.

RMMM

KLANK

RATTLE

...BUT HE'D EASILY ESCAPE A NORMAL PRISON.

THIS RESTRAINING DEVICE DESIGNED BY THE HERO ASSOCIATION HAS HIM UNDER CONTROL...

BEYOND THIS DOOR...

WE'VE ARRIVED.

...IS YOUR NEW HOME...

...SPEED-O'-SOUND SONIC.

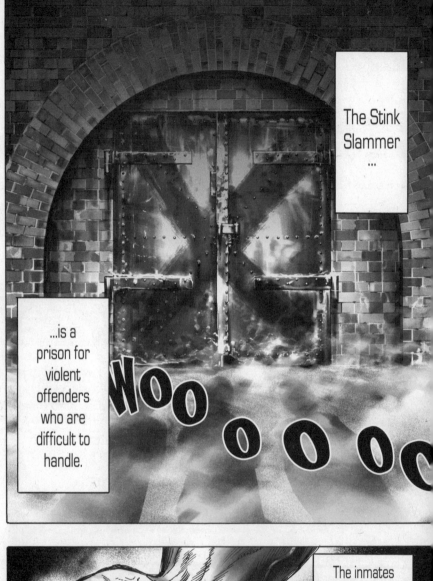

The Stink Slammer ...

...is a prison for violent offenders who are difficult to handle.

WOOOOOO

The inmates have monstrous strength sufficient to pry open iron bars with their bare hands.

Truly **uncommon** criminals lurk here.

Some require isolation to stop them from harming the mental well-being of others.

They can use everyday items to make keys, weapons or poisons.

HYUK HYUK HYUK!

ANOTHER SCRAWNY DUDE.

TUMP

TUMP

YOU GOT IT.

CLOMP

GO.

HEH... LET'S *PLAY*.

OOPS. YOU BUMPED INTO ME.

WATCH WHERE YOU'RE—

BUMP

POP

HUH?!

HMPH
...

HE DISLOCATED MY SHOULDER!

YAOW!!

LOSER
...

LEMME SHOW YOU HOW IT'S DONE.

WHAT'RE YOU IN FOR?

YO, NEW DUDE.

GUESS THAT'S WHY YER HERE.

YOU MAY BE KINDA TOUGH...

HEH.

YOU LOOK FEISTY.

ONE: NEW DUDES MUST ALWAYS OBEY OLDER—

GET LOST.

...BUT LISTEN UP.

WE GOT RULES HERE.

HUH?

...

W

HOK

GA HA HA! BEAT 'IM GOOD !!!

IDIOT. HE ANGERED *DESTROYER JOHN*.

I HEARD YOUR CHEEK-BONE SHATTER—

HAH HAH! I NEVER HOLD BACK!

SINCE
WHEN?!

THERE!
BY
THE
WALL
!!

WHAT
HAP-
PENED
?!

HUH?!
WHERE'D
THAT
DUDE
GO?!

GYAOUCH!!

AND I
CAME IN
THROUGH
MULTIPLE
HEAVY
DOORS
...

A THICK
STEEL
WALL...

NO USE
WORRYIN'
OVER
ESCAPE!

...AND
NO WIN-
DOWS.

THINK
ABOUT HOW
TO SPEND
YOUR LIFE
HERE!

I SEEN YOUNG GUYS LOSE THEIR *MARBLES* IN HERE!

IT'S MY ONLY ENTERTAINMENT!

NO SALVATION NEITHER! HEE HEE!

AIN'T GOT NO *MORALS* IN HERE!

JUST IMAGININ' IT GETS ME DROOLIN'! HEE HEE!

THAT PROUD FACE WILL CONTORT WHEN IT HITS BOTTOM!!

?

HEH HEH. IS IT ANY DIFFERENT OUTSIDE?

NO MORALS, HUH?

AND I GUESS EVEN VIOLENT CRIMINALS HAVE TO RESPECT EACH OTHER, OR COMMUNAL LIFE BREAKS DOWN.

IT'S ADMIRABLE FOR LOSERS TO CONGREGATE, CREATE THEIR OWN "ORDER" AND HOLD EACH OTHER UP.

...?

BUT I'M DIFFERENT.

IT'S ALL ABOUT WEAK-NESS.

BY *KILLING* YOU ALL!

I'LL BE COMFORT-ABLE HERE. KNOW HOW?

W-WHY YOU...!!!

?!

CRIK

CRAK

YOU WANNA CLIMB THE RANKS HERE? START WITH *ME*.

HE SEEMS CONFIDENT.

YOU WANT I SHOULD BREAK HIM?

WAIT. I'LL DO IT.

I'M THE ONLY ONE WHO'S EVER ROBBED A BANK BARE-HANDED!

I'M WARNING YOU. I USE KENPO.

BUT WHAT'S THE POINT IF YOU GET CAUGHT?

HERE I COME!

GR-RA-A-A...

SHH! BOSS WOKE UP!

QUIET... BE STILL!

WHAT'S THE MATTER?

YOUR ATTITUDE SUDDENLY CHANGED.

BOSS INSISTS...

...WE INMATES GET ALONG.

SO IF I BEAT HIM, THEN...

DON'T EVEN *THINK* ABOUT IT!

BOSS?

YOU SHOULDN'T HAVE YELLED!

PLEASE. JUST COOPERATE OR WE'LL *ALL* PAY.

SORRY...

THAT WAS UNTIL BOSS CAME!!

IT'S A LITTLE DIFFERENT NOW!

HOLD ON A SECOND...

WHAT WAS THAT ABOUT *MORALS*?

I WONDER WHAT HE'S LIKE?

THEY'RE SCARED TO DEATH OF HIM.

AS PUNISH-MENT LATER...

...I'LL DEEP KISS ALL OF THEM.

WERE THEY BULLYING THE NEW GUY?

#4188 SONIC

FWIP

THOSE RASCALS...

BOSS CAME ABOUT ONE YEAR AGO.

HE CAUGHT A MAN WITH AN A-CLASS BOUNTY ON HIS HEAD AND CAME HERE WITH HIM.

Former A-Class wanted man

HE'S A *SHELL* OF A MAN NOW.

WORD IS HE *WANTED* TO BE HERE.

APPARENTLY THE GUY HE CAUGHT...

...WAS EXACTLY HIS TYPE.

BOSS REALIZED SOMETHING HERE.

ATTACKING NORMAL GUYS IS WRONG...

I DON'T LIKE WHERE THIS IS GOING...

IF WE'RE GOOD, HE KISSES US ON THE CHEEK, BUT...

BOSS'S REACH IS LONG...

EVEN A CRUSTY VETERAN LIKE ME IS SCARED...

IS HE FRIENDS WITH THE GUARDS OR SOMETHING?

ONLY BOSS CAN GET OUT.

HEH! I KNEW THERE WAS A WAY!

YOU SAID HE BREAKS OUT?

YOU WOULDN'T SAY THAT IN FRONT OF BOSS.

EARLIER, YOU WAS TALKIN' ABOUT WEAKNESS.

A HERO IS ATTEMPTING TO PREVENT THEIR ADVANCE.

THE CREATURES APPEARING IN CITY J CLAIM TO BE FROM THE CLAN OF THE SEAFOLK.

THEY'RE GOING TO HURT STINGER !!!

OH NO !!

ONLY BOSS CAN MAKE A GETAWAY.

GUARDS WILL BE HERE IN FIVE SECONDS. STEP OUTSIDE AND YOU'RE SWISS CHEESE!

BOSS MADE ANOTHER HOLE.

SHOULD WE GO TOO?

WHO IS HE?

HE'S MORE POWERFUL THAN HAMMERHEAD'S SUIT!

WEEOOO

HE'S A CLASS-S HERO.

HE'S *PURI-PURI PRISONER.*

HM? WHERE'D THE NEW GUY GO?

4 Giant Meteor (End)

SHALL WE GO?

...

SUPERSALE FRESH SEAFOOD FAIR!

RAW SAURY (SASHIMI) ¥298

WE'LL HAVE TO HURRY.

Bonus (End)

END NOTES

PAGE 8, PANEL 1:
The back of Saitama's shirt says Chicago and the front says Bulls.

PAGE 10, PANEL 1:
Saitama's bookshelf contains ONE's book *Mob Psycho 100*.

BA DUMP
BA DUMP

ONE-PUNCH MAN
VOLUME 4
SHONEN JUMP MANGA EDITION

STORY BY | ONE
ART BY | YUSUKE MURATA

TRANSLATION | JOHN WERRY
TOUCH-UP ART AND LETTERING | JAMES GAUBATZ
DESIGN | FAWN LAU
SHONEN JUMP SERIES EDITOR | JOHN BAE
GRAPHIC NOVEL EDITOR | JENNIFER LEBLANC

Printed in the U.S.A.

Published by VIZ Media, LLC
P.O. Box 77010
San Francisco, CA 94107

10 9 8 7 6
First printing, January 2016
Sixth printing, July 2023

VIZ MEDIA
viz.com

SHONEN JUMP

EYESHIELD 21

STORY BY RIICHIRO INAGAKI
ART BY YUSUKE MURATA

From the artist of *One-Punch Man!*

Wimpy Sena Kobayakawa has been running away from
bullies all his life. But when the football gear comes
on, things change—Sena's speed and uncanny ability
to elude big bullies just might give him what it takes to
become a great high school football hero! Catch all the
bone-crushing action and slapstick comedy of Japan's
hottest football manga!

Hikaru no Go

Story by YUMI HOTTA
Art by TAKESHI OBATA

SHONEN JUMP GRAPHIC NOVEL
volume 1

The breakthrough series by Takeshi Obata, the artist of Death Note!

Hikaru Shindo is like any sixth-grader in Japan: a pretty normal schoolboy with a penchant for antics. One day, he finds an old bloodstained Go board in his grandfather's attic. Trapped inside the Go board is Fujiwara-no-Sai, the ghost of an ancient Go master. In one fateful moment, Sai becomes a part of Hikaru's consciousness and together, through thick and thin, they make an unstoppable Go-playing team.

Will they be able to defeat Go players who have dedicated their lives to the game? And will Sai achieve the "Divine Move" so he'll finally be able to rest in peace? Find out in this *Shonen Jump* classic!

RATED
A
ALL AGES
ratings.viz.com

MEDIA

www.shonenjump.com

www.viz.com

STOP!

YOU'RE READING THE WRONG WAY!

★ ONE-PUNCH MAN READS FROM RIGHT TO LEFT, STARTING IN THE UPPER-RIGHT CORNER. JAPANESE IS READ FROM RIGHT TO LEFT, MEANING THAT ACTION, SOUND EFFECTS, AND WORD-BALLOON ORDER ARE COMPLETELY REVERSED FROM ENGLISH ORDER.